CW00672444

Horrid and Hideous History

Interactive Quiz

Managing Editors: Simon Melhuish and Sarah Wells

Series Editor: Nikole G Bamford

Designer: Linley J Clode

Writer: Paul Lucas

Cover Design: Radio

Published by
The Lagoon Group
PO Box 311, KT2 5QW, UK
PO Box 990676, Boston, MA 02199, USA

ISBN: 1904797563

© LAGOON BOOKS 2004

Lagoon Books is a trade mark of
Lagoon Trading Company Limited.
All rights reserved.

www.intelliquestbooks.com

Printed in China

IntelliQuest

UNIQUE BOOK CODE	029

Instructions

First of all make sure you
have a Quizmo —

Find the book's unique code (this
appears at the top of this page).
Use the **<** and **>** buttons to scroll
to this number on the Quizmo screen.
Press the ↵ button to enter the
code, and you're ready to go.

Use the **< >** scroll buttons to select
the question number you want to
answer. Press the **A**, **B**, **C**, or **D**
button to enter your chosen answer.

If you are correct the green light beside
the button you pressed will flash. You can then
use the scroll button to move on to another question.

If your answer is incorrect, the red light beside the
button you pressed will flash.

Don't worry, you can try again and again until you have the correct answer, OR move on to another question. (Beware: the more times you guess incorrectly, the lower your final percentage score will be!)

You can finish the quiz at any point – just press the ⟳ button to find out your score and rank as follows:

75% or above	The more grisly it is the better you like it!
50% – 74%	You certainly know your nasty past!
25% – 49%	The days of yore are a bit of a yawn to you!
Less than 25%	Your head for history is horrid!

If you do press the ⟳ button to find out your score, this will end your session and you will have to use the ⟳ to start again!

HAVE FUN!

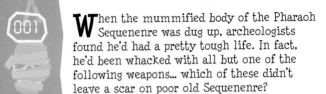

001

When the mummified body of the Pharaoh Sequenenre was dug up, archeologists found he'd had a pretty tough life. In fact, he'd been whacked with all but one of the following weapons... which of these didn't leave a scar on poor old Sequenenre?

A) Axe
B) Mace
C) Spear
D) Club

002

At least Sequenenre's problems ended when he died. What horrible thing happened to Queen Henattawy shortly AFTER she'd died?

A) She caught fire
B) Her face fell off
C) She was ground up and used as dog food
D) She was beheaded

003

Rameses's mummy is the only one in history to what?

A) Get up and speak
B) Be wrapped in black bandages
C) Be served up on a dinner plate
D) Be issued a passport

The Ancient Egyptians

The Egyptians sometimes used crocodile excrement as what?

    A) Toothpaste
    B) Shampoo
    C) Eyewash
    D) Deodorant

Tomb robbers thought they could escape any curses left in a burial chamber by knocking what off the sarcophagi?

    A) The feet
    B) The heads
    C) The noses
    D) The hands

A laborer in Ancient Egypt worked how many days before getting two days' rest?

    A) 2
    B) 10
    C) 20
    D) 30

007

What was a wabet in Ancient Egypt?

A) A rabbit

B) A tomb robber

C) A human sacrifice

D) A place where mummies were embalmed

008

The Egyptians tested whether a woman was pregnant by placing what in her flesh?

A) An onion

B) A fig

C) A live dove

D) A stick of celery

009

How many layers of bandages does a mummy have?

A) 1

B) 3

C) 20

D) 100

The Ancient Egyptians

What was the penalty for robbing a tomb in ancient Egypt?

A) Death by crucifixion
B) Death by impalement
C) Death by stoning
D) Five hundred lines

What did the Egyptians sometimes use to make false eyes?

A) Eggs
B) Pebbles
C) Sea shells
D) Onions

Which of these has NOT been found inside a mummy's body?

A) Sawdust
B) Rags
C) Sand
D) Sage and onion stuffing

013

What, in Ancient Egyptian belief, was Amentet?

- **A)** The underworld
- **B)** The God of War
- **C)** A three-headed dog that guarded the gates to heaven
- **D)** The devil

014

What was the name of the book that described the rituals to be performed when an Ancient Egyptian died?

- **A)** The Book Of The Mummy
- **B)** The Book Of The Dead
- **C)** The Book Of The Ghosts
- **D)** The Book Of The Stiffs

015

Before being mummified the body is washed in what?

- **A)** Camel urine
- **B)** Olive oil
- **C)** Water from the Nile
- **D)** Goat slobber

What was contained in the four canopic jars placed next to a mummy?

A) Lager
B) The internal organs of the body
C) Curses to protect the body from tomb raiders
D) Various foods to help the spirit in the afterlife

These jars were guarded by the spirits of the four sons of Horus, who were represented on the jars with the heads of different animals. Which of these animal's heads is NOT featured on the canopic jars?

A) Baboon
B) Heron
C) Hawk
D) Jackal

Which organ was left inside the body after mummification?

A) The heart
B) The brain
C) The liver
D) The appendix

019

What method was used to remove the brain of a dead body?

A) The top of the head was sawn off

B) A hole was bored in the side of the head

C) The brain was pulled out through the nose

D) Acid was squirted into the ears

020

The Ancient Egyptians slept on pillows made of what?

A) Thorns

B) Human hair

C) Inflated camel bladders

D) Stone

021

One of the most famous mummies is that of Tutankhamen. When archeologists x-rayed his body, they found that what important bone was missing?

A) His left leg bone

B) His right eye socket

C) His breastbone

D) His pelvis

The Ancient Egyptians

Tutankhamen was also missing what?

- **A)** His right ear
- **B)** His nose
- **C)** His fingernails
- **D)** His mum

Tutankhamen's body was stuck fast in his sarcophagus, so what did the man who performed his autopsy do to get it out?

- **A)** He turned the sarcophagus upside down and shook it
- **B)** He blasted the body out with dynamite
- **C)** He carefully chipped the body out with a tiny hammer
- **D)** He cut Tutankhamen's head and arms off

A whole bunch of grave offerings were found in Tutankhamen's tomb, including what?

- **A)** 58 pairs of slippers
- **B)** 130 walking sticks
- **C)** 240 hats
- **D)** 19 roof tiles

The Ancient Egyptians

025

People say kids grow up fast these days, but Tutankhamen had married and become ruler of the most powerful country on earth by the time he was what age?

A) 9
B) 12
C) 15
D) 17

026

The oldest mummy ever found in Egypt dates from 3200 BC and is known as –?

A) Ginger
B) Wrinkles
C) Old Dude
D) Grandma

027

To prevent graying hair, Egyptians prepared an ointment made from what?

A) Crocodile fat
B) Hyena's tail
C) Rhino horn
D) The blood of a black bull

Which of these happened at a Roman horse race?

A) The winning horse was killed

B) The losing horse was killed

C) The winning rider was killed

D) The losing rider was killed

What was the vomitorium in Roman times?

A) A sporting event in which the winner was the one who could puke the most

B) A hospital for those with sleeping sickness

C) A temple to the God of Blowing Chunks

D) A side room to be sick in at great feasts

Of which Roman Emperor did Aurelius Victor write 'he spent the rest of his life so disgracefully that it is disgusting and shameful to record the existence of anyone of this kind, let alone that he was ruler of the world?'

A) Nero

B) Caesar

C) Vitellius

D) Caligula

031

A t the end of a gladiator fight, the crowd would sometimes shout 'Iugula!' What did this mean?

    A) Spare him!

    B) Kill him!

    C) Bravo!

    D) We want our money back!

032

H ow did the Romans cross the terrible swampy fenlands of East Anglia when they were conquering Britain?

    A) They used their shields as makeshift boats

    B) On stilts

    C) They drained the swamps with giant pumps made from oak trees

    D) They swam through using bamboo shoots as scuba diving masks

033

A t the time of the Roman Conquests, what were fashionable amongst ancient Britons?

    A) Mammoth hair wigs

    B) Horned helmets

    C) Curly shoes

    D) Long moustaches

The Romans

The Celts who resisted the Roman invasion had –?

034

A) Elephants
B) Green beards
C) Bleached spiky hair
D) Battle goats

One of the most successful Celtic leaders was Queen Boudicca, who attacked London and killed a reported 70,000 people. She was the leader of which tribe?

035

A) The Bloggarts
B) The Khalahari
C) The Iceni
D) The Boudicceans

According to the Roman historian Tacitus, how did Boudicca die?

036

A) She drank poison to avoid being captured
B) She was crucified upside down after being captured
C) She was shot in the eye with an arrow in battle
D) She was involved in a chariot crash at Piccadilly Circus

037

Archeologists believe Boudicca's body is where?

    A) Scattered all over Piccadilly Circus

    B) At the bottom of the Thames River

    C) In a small church in Cornwall

    D) Under platform 8 at King's Cross station in London

038

What, in Roman times, was an 'Isicia Omentata'?

    A) A death warrant

    B) A slave who had to clean all the gore up after a gladiator fight

    C) A silent but deadly fart

    D) An early form of hamburger

039

Roman streets had public toilets – well, sort of. If you were desperate to go, you would head for a street corner where you'd have to urinate in a –?

    A) Hole in the ground

    B) Pottery jar

    C) Hollow tree trunk

    D) Slave's pocket

The Romans

Which Roman Emperor was once captured by pirates?

A) Caesar
B) Severus
C) Nero
D) Caligula

The Roman Emperor Nero is famous for 'fiddling while Rome burned.' But when he wasn't playing musical instruments, he busied himself with much more horrible pastimes. Which of these did he NOT do?

A) Tried to kill his mother, failed, so tried again, and succeeded
B) Kicked his pregnant wife to death
C) Had his father boiled alive in a vat of wine
D) Had his ex-wife's head cut off and sent to his new wife as a present

---

The Roman citizen Bulla lived around AD 229 and was a famous what?

A) Highwayman
B) Jester
C) Executioner
D) Gladiator

The Romans

 043
The Romans thought you needed money after you died, so they put a coin in the dead person's –?

    A) Mouth
    B) Ear
    C) Hand
    D) Backside

 044
The Romans used poisonous lead in their what?

    A) Arrows
    B) Drinking vessels
    C) Shampoo
    D) Bubble bath

 045
Which of these did the Romans use as toothpaste?

    A) Snot
    B) Excrement
    C) Urine
    D) Ear wax

How did the Roman Emperor Frederick die?

046

- **A)** He choked on a grape
- **B)** He jumped into a river with his armor on and drowned
- **C)** He went to inspect a prison and was crucified by mistake
- **D)** He was kicked to death by a group of schoolchildren

The Emperor Nero once had someone put to death for what?

047

- **A)** Looking at him in a funny way
- **B)** Having a stupid name
- **C)** Being a better actor than him
- **D)** Having the same haircut as him

What was the nickname of the Emperor Vitellius?

048

- **A)** The Beast
- **B)** The Glutton
- **C)** The Stink
- **D)** The Bed-wetter

049

A 'retarius' was a gladiator who fought with what?

- **A)** A tripod
- **B)** A net
- **C)** A hammer
- **D)** Two swords

050

M inerva was the Roman goddess of what?

- **A)** Schoolchildren
- **B)** Death
- **C)** Bodily functions
- **D)** War

051

W hy was Caesar always shown wearing a wreath in portraits?

- **A)** The portrait artists wanted to make fun of him
- **B)** The wreath is a symbol of bravery
- **C)** He wanted to cover up his baldness
- **D)** The wreath covered up a birthmark on his head

Rome became a republic when their extremely cruel and fearsome King was overthrown. What was this most feared tyrant's name?

  A) Ethel The Bad
  B) Brutus The Brave
  C) Tarquin The Proud
  D) Percival The Soft

Why did the Romans sometimes deliberately burn their bread?

  A) To try and remove the stink of their homes
  B) They thought it would ward off disease
  C) As an offering to the God of food
  D) Burnt bread was considered a delicacy in Roman times

Which of these did the Romans invent?

  A) Concrete
  B) The bow and arrow
  C) Pottery
  D) Gunpowder

055

What did the Romans sometimes eat as a light snack?

- **A)** Bats
- **B)** Lice
- **C)** Mice
- **D)** Worms

056

If you signed up for the Roman army, how long did you have to serve for before you could decide it wasn't for you?

- **A)** Twenty-five years
- **B)** A year
- **C)** Five years
- **D)** Two weeks

057

Some Roman soldiers carried a 'pilum.' What was it?

- **A)** A spear designed to be thrown
- **B)** A stick with a sponge on it to clean your behind with
- **C)** A vial of poison to be drunk if you were captured
- **D)** A sundial to tell the time with

The Romans

The slave Spartacus organized an uprising against Rome which very nearly succeeded. Unfortunately for Spartacus, he was double crossed by –?

A) His brother
B) The Roman General Marcus Crassus
C) His teacher
D) Pirates

Rome eventually crushed the rebellion and crucified the survivors along the course of their main road, the Appian Way. So, if you were heading to Rome at this time, you would have had to walk past how many crucified men?

A) 30
B) 400
C) 6,000
D) 70,000

Slaves who cut food up for wealthy Romans were called what?

A) Knives
B) Spoons
C) Scissors
D) Forki

The Romans

061

When Rome conquered a country, the young men of that country were often forced to join the Roman army. What did some do to try and get out of this?

- **A)** Break their own leg so they couldn't march
- **B)** Blind themselves
- **C)** Pretend to have a headache
- **D)** Cut one of their thumbs off so they couldn't hold a sword

062

The Romans used to have fabulous chariot races at the Circus Maximus, and often Roman citizens would bet on who would win. In order to try and guess who stood the best chance, they would sometimes...

- **A)** Bribe the charioteers to give them inside information
- **B)** Analyze the excrement of the horses to see which ones had been eating properly
- **C)** Pray to the God of Charioteers for advice
- **D)** Taste the urine of the horses and determine the fitness of the horse by how salty it was

The Romans

Before the race, some Romans would scratch curses into tablets of stone asking the Gods to hurt a rival charioteer. What were these called?

A) Curse tablets
B) Dark stones
C) Scratch spells
D) Death songs

During one period of the Roman Empire you could be executed for what?

A) Not wearing a toga
B) Sneezing in public
C) Being cruel to dogs
D) Singing insulting songs

One Roman doctor believed you could make loose teeth firm again by strapping what to your jaw?

A) A frog
B) A live dove
C) An onion
D) A golden coin

The Emperor Caesar was assassinated in what way?

A) He was stabbed 23 times
B) He was strangled
C) He was poisoned
D) He had his throat cut

One of the reasons Caesar was so unpopular was because he'd started acting like a King instead of an Emperor. Which of these actions was deemed to be evidence of his desire to be treated like a King?

A) He started wearing a crown
B) He started wearing a purple toga
C) He started wearing red boots
D) He started sitting on a throne

One of the more peculiar Roman Emperors, Heliogabalus, had a collection of what?

A) Giraffes
B) Cobwebs
C) Pebbles
D) Stamps

The Romans

Which of these delicious dishes could you find on the menu of a Roman feast?

- **A)** Stuffed thrushes
- **B)** Boiled crocodile
- **C)** Roast monkey
- **D)** Slave pie

You might like to wash that down with a special Roman sauce made from –?

- **A)** Moldy peaches
- **B)** Rotten fish guts
- **C)** Bat's blood
- **D)** Donkey's eyeballs

If you were lucky enough to be a guest at a feast thrown by the Emperor Heliogabalus, you might well find yourself eating the brains of what?

- **A)** Elephants
- **B)** Ostriches
- **C)** Leopards
- **D)** Sharks

072 Which of these dreadful things were the Romans responsible for introducing into Britain?

    A) The Black Death
    B) Compulsory schools
    C) Teachers
    D) Stinging nettles

073 Which of these did the Emperor Caligula attempt to make a senator?

    A) His dead father
    B) His shadow
    C) The man who used to run his bath for him
    D) His favorite horse

074 The Romans had a particular type of slave called 'sparsiones.' What was their job?

    A) To spray perfume over smelly crowds
    B) To wipe wealthy Romans' behinds
    C) To take the blame when a wealthy Roman farted
    D) To lie by the door as a human draught-excluder

The Romans

Which of these did the Emperor Elagabalus like to do?

    A) Juggle with the severed heads of his enemies

    B) Watch six-year-old children fight to the death in gladiatorial combat

    C) Dance around altars dressed as a woman

    D) Swim in an artificial lake of wine

The Emperor Domitian liked to spend his time doing what?

    A) Playing with toy soldiers

    B) Torturing flies

    C) Racing pigs

    D) Talking to chickens

When Romans invaded Britain, they found priests called Druids living there. What did a Druid do when he wanted the help of the spirits?

    A) He chanted a spell whilst setting fire to a dead cat

    B) He slept inside a slaughtered bull

    C) He put his head in a bucket of puke

    D) He climbed an oak tree naked

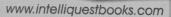

078

When a Druid wanted to see into the future he would –?

    A) Drink the blood of an ox
    B) Hang upside down from a yew tree
    C) Chew the flesh of a dead dog
    D) Stroke a vole

079

Like father, like son – which of these did the Emperor Nero's father NOT do?

    A) Murdered someone for refusing to drink all the booze he'd bought for them
    B) Gouged someone's eyes out for criticizing him
    C) Bit the nose off someone who had just winked at him
    D) Ran over a child just for a bit of fun

080

If you were given the job of 'lanista' in Ancient Rome, you would be expected to do what?

    A) Make swords
    B) Carry long distance messages
    C) Clean toilets
    D) Train gladiators

In the ninth century in Ireland, the Vikings imposed a 'nose tax.' How did it get its name?

081

A) Because you were taxed on the size of your nose

B) Because if you didn't pay it you had your nose cut off

C) Because it was a fine on how smelly your house was

D) Nobody nose

How was King Edmund Ironside killed?

082

A) Throttled while sleeping

B) Thrown to the lions

C) Drowned while in the bath

D) Stabbed while on the toilet

Who killed King Edward I?

083

A) His father-in-law

B) His brother

C) His step-mother

D) His court jester

084

Vikings used to wash their clothes in –?

A) Blood
B) Beer
C) Milk
D) Cow urine

085

The Vikings sometimes used the skulls of their victims as what?

A) Drinking vessels
B) Footballs
C) Necklaces
D) Candle holders

086

At about what age could you expect to die in 5th century Britain?

A) 12
B) 30
C) 75
D) 45

The Dark Ages

Pope Formosus was interrogated by Pope Stephen VII in 896 and put on trial for a variety of crimes. Why was this unusual?

    A) Pope Formosus was dead at the time
    B) Pope Formosus was discovered to be a woman
    C) Pope Formosus was a cocker spaniel
    D) Pope Formosus was only six

It's thought that the Saxons got their name for a weapon they carried called a 'seax.' What kind of weapon was it?

    A) A club
    B) A bow
    C) An axe
    D) A sword

The Franks were also named after a weapon they carried – the 'franca.' What sort of deadly device was a 'franca?'

    A) A curved sword
    B) A giant double-headed axe
    C) A type of javelin
    D) A catapult

090

What does the word 'Viking' mean?

A) Man with horns
B) Bearded warrior
C) Bloody sword
D) A pirate raid

091

Which of these is the name of a REAL Viking?

A) Halfdown Goldenballs
B) Ragnor Hairy-Trousers
C) Ivar The Ticklish
D) Svein Sausage-Breath

092

How did the Viking Erik The Red get his name?

A) He covered his face in blood before going into battle
B) He dressed from head to foot in red
C) He had bright red hair
D) He had a red birth mark on his face

The Dark Ages

A lot of houses in The Dark Ages had walls made with what?

A) Cow bones

B) Human skulls

C) Bear fur

D) Pig's excrement

W hat did the Anglo-Saxons eat to cure themselves of the worms that infested their stomachs?

A) Toadstools

B) Horse excrement

C) Poisonous bracken

D) Worm-infested dogs

C hildren in The Dark Ages used to play a game with the bones from a pig's trotter. What was the game called?

A) Grand Theft Auto

B) Pig In A Poke

C) Ducks And Drakes

D) Chuckstones

096

If you wanted to become a monk in The Dark Ages, you had to get up at two in the morning, pray seven times a day, and work in the fields when you weren't praying. On top of that you were beaten with sticks if you did anything wrong and fed mainly on porridge and bread. At what age would you set off for 'Monk School?'

A) 16
B) 5
C) 7
D) 12

097

In 685, the English King Ecgfrith led his army north to attack the Picts in Scotland. Only one person lived to tell the tale. What happened to the rest?

A) They were all killed in a battle that lasted 16 hours
B) They were slaughtered when they walked into a trap and couldn't escape
C) They all died of a mysterious plague
D) They were all killed after they ended up fighting each other in an argument about who hated the Picts the most

Which part of Robert The Bruce was removed from his body and taken on a crusade to The Holy Land in 1329?

    A) His right hand
    B) His head
    C) His tongue
    D) His heart

Why did King Henry I probably not look forward to kissing his wife Matilda?

    A) She only ever ate raw onions
    B) She had teeth like a vampire
    C) She used to kiss the sores of lepers
    D) She used to drink her own urine

What was the nickname of the Scottish King Malcolm IV?

    A) The Sweetheart
    B) The Schoolgirl
    C) The Maiden
    D) The Lady

101 In the 14th century children were beaten at Eton College for –?

- **A)** Not drinking beer at breakfast
- **B)** Not smoking
- **C)** Not swearing
- **D)** Not trying to bunk off school

102 One way people tried to ward off plague in The Middle Ages was to bathe in –?

- **A)** A child's vomit
- **B)** Water a witch had spat in
- **C)** Cow dung
- **D)** Their own urine

103 The first recorded use of toilet paper was in what year?

- **A)** 1300
- **B)** 1058
- **C)** 986
- **D)** 1420

The Middle Ages

The reign of William The Conqueror didn't begin all that well. At his coronation in the newly opened Westminster Abbey, the shouts of well-wishers were mistaken by guards outside the church to be a sign that something had gone wrong. They were so alarmed that they –?

- **A)** Burnt down the Abbey
- **B)** Burst into the Abbey and slaughtered several guests
- **C)** Burnt down several neighboring houses
- **D)** Rode off all the way back to France

If the start of William's reign was bad, the end was even worse. What do you think happened at his funeral?

- **A)** His corpse fell out of the coffin and rolled around the church
- **B)** His corpse burst open and filled the church with a foul stench
- **C)** A candle set fire to his coffin and his body went up in flames
- **D)** The roof of the church caved in and killed 32 members of the congregation

106 Who wrote an epitaph for himself that read: 'Here lies the worst of Kings and most miserable of men?'

A) William The Conqueror
B) Philip The Gloomy
C) Henry I
D) Robert III

107 What did The Archbishop of Canterbury read in the 'Toledo Letter' that caused him to fast for three days?

A) That the Pope thought he was too fat
B) That the King had signed the Archbishop's death warrant
C) That The Black Death was a punishment from God
D) That the world was about to end

108 The name 'Pauperes Christi' was used to refer to monks, hermits and –?

A) Lepers
B) Slaves
C) Peasants
D) Pickpockets

In the 14th century, you often had to bury your dead relatives yourself. Gravediggers were particularly reluctant to dig graves for –?

A) Witches
B) Victims of the plague
C) Children
D) Debt collectors

The 'flagellants' were a religious group who believed the way to find salvation was to –?

A) Catch leprosy
B) Starve yourself to death
C) Whip yourself
D) Get drunk

A poisonous fungus affecting flour caused many people in the Middle Ages to catch a terrible disease which could lead to your arms and legs dropping off. What was it called?

A) Dropsy
B) St Anthony's Fire
C) Willow Burn
D) Leprosy

112

A popular (and completely horrible) game in the Middle Ages was to tie your hands behind your back and try to –?

A) Kick a dog to death with your bare feet

B) Beat a cat to death with your head

C) Eat a live chicken with your teeth

D) Play football with a hedgehog

113

Most minor operations in this period were carried out by –?

A) Barbers

B) Butchers

C) Monks

D) Nuns

114

In 1364 a man was hired to paint red crosses around the Louvre art gallery and its gardens in the hope that it might prevent what?

A) Witches

B) Thieves

C) People urinating

D) Plague

If you heard a shout of 'Gardez l'eau!' in 13th century France, you could expect what shortly afterwards?

A) Someone's head to be chopped off

B) The King to pass by

C) A cart of plague victims to pass by

D) A pot of urine to be thrown out of a window

What did Robert III of Scotland want to have happen to his body after he died?

A) For it to be eaten by his friends at a feast

B) For it to be fired from the castle in a giant catapult

C) For it to be buried in a dung heap

D) For it to be fed to his favorite dog

When Pedro of Portugal was crowned King what was one of the first things he did?

A) Dig up his dead mistress and make her Queen

B) Execute the previous King

C) Ban moustaches

D) Drink poison

118 **W**ho were the 'shaveldours' in 14th century England?

- **A)** Grave diggers
- **B)** Barbers
- **C)** Excrement shovelers
- **D)** Gentleman robbers

119 **A**ll manner of weird and wonderful 'cures' were thought up in the Middle Ages. For example, if you had whooping cough in Lincolnshire, England, you'd probably be given –?

- **A)** A bath in cold cat's urine
- **B)** Fried mice
- **C)** A goblet of warm goat's blood
- **D)** A whack on the back with a broom

120 **W**hereas in Yorkshire, England, if you had the same disease you'd be fed –?

- **A)** Owls
- **B)** Lice
- **C)** Toads
- **D)** Turnips

The Middle Ages

At about the same time in Scotland, it was thought you could cure a fever by rubbing what between your hands?

    A) A live mole
    B) A dead chicken
    C) A piece of cheese
    D) Raw onions

Which of these did the Aristocracy use as toilet paper in the Middle Ages?

    A) Nettles
    B) Bear's fur
    C) Live kittens
    D) Goose feathers

What did 'gong scourers' do?

    A) Shoveled the excrement from rich people's houses
    B) Entertained at feasts by pulling faces
    C) Scoured rubbish tips for scrap metal
    D) Robbed graves

124

King Henry I had the most illegitimate children of any British King in history. How many did he have?

    A) 1,476
    B) 72
    C) 106
    D) 21

125

Robert The Bruce's army took over an English fort at Kelso by disguising themselves as what?

    A) Cows
    B) Rat-catchers
    C) Nuns
    D) Trees

126

In just four years, The Black Death reduced the population of Europe by –?

    A) 2%
    B) 30%
    C) 10%
    D) 95%

The Middle Ages

It was thought at one time that you could cure plague by eating what?

A) Live eels
B) The scabs of a plague victim's sores
C) The tail of a dog
D) Rats

127

In China during the Middle Ages the devious Tseng Kung Liang described how to make a what?

A) Booby-trapped cat
B) Urine-filled trap
C) Fart gas grenade
D) Bomb made of excrement

128

And in South America, The Aztecs were opening a new temple to their sun god Tenochtitlan. To ensure Tenochtitlan was happy, they sacrificed what?

A) 1,000 goats
B) 2,000 dogs
C) 24,000 slaves and captured prisoners
D) 6,000 children

129

130

In Henry VIII's navy, sailors took pepper to try and stop themselves doing what?

A) Scratching
B) Spewing
C) Farting
D) Catching the plague

131

Why was the Duke Of Medina Sidonia, the commander of The Spanish Armada that attacked Britain in 1588, such a strange choice?

A) He suffered from seasickness
B) He was blind
C) He was only twelve years old
D) He was British

132

Henry VIII ordered more executions than any other British King. About how many people is he thought to have ordered to be killed?

A) 30
B) 1,000,000
C) 2,000
D) 75,000

Queen Elizabeth I was the first Queen to have a what?

- **A)** Bodyguard
- **B)** False leg
- **C)** Crown
- **D)** Flushing toilet

The slaughtering of one army or another was more or less a regular occurrence around this time. But the massacre of an English army at Hornshole in 1514 was a touch out of the ordinary because it was carried out largely by –?

- **A)** Women
- **B)** Children
- **C)** Pensioners
- **D)** Lepers

Who were 'groundlings?'

- **A)** People who had to stand up when they went to the theater
- **B)** Gravediggers
- **C)** People who lived in underground caves
- **D)** People who believed the earth was flat

136 Kids at Edinburgh High School knew how to stand up to their teachers. In 1595 they launched an armed rebellion in which an officer of the law was killed. What was the spark for this bloodshed?

A) They'd been told they had to start wearing short trousers

B) One of the pupils had been sentenced to fifty lashes for forgetting his gym clothes

C) They'd had their holidays cut

D) They'd been forced to start learning mathematics

137 King James VI wrote a book about what?

A) Witches

B) Beer

C) Farting

D) Ghosts

138 Who was crowned Tsar of Russia in 1547?

A) Ivan The Terrible

B) Igor The Butcher

C) Boris The Bone Crusher

D) Vlad The Impaler

In the 1500s, Pope Clement 8th gave his blessing to what had previously been called 'Satan's drink.' What was this devilish brew?

A) Beer
B) Coffee
C) Tea
D) Lemonade

139

One of the wives of Henry VIII, Anne Boleyn, had which feature?

A) Two heads
B) One leg
C) Eleven fingers
D) A huge behind

140

How many of Henry VIII's wives were executed?

A) 1
B) 2
C) 3
D) 4

141

142

After Anne Boleyn was executed, no coffin was provided for her, so they stuffed her body into –?

   A) A trough that had been used to feed pigs

   B) A cupboard that had been used to hang chain mail in

   C) A chest that had been used to carry arrows

   D) An iron box that had been used to carry the executioner's axe

143

The Scots were fond of 'wirrying' witches. If you were a witch, what was worrying about 'wirrying'?

   A) It meant you were about to get stoned to death

   B) It meant you were about to get strangled to death

   C) It meant you were about to get burnt to death

   D) It meant you were about to be tied to a boulder and rolled down a hill

The Tudor and the Stuart Ages

In the Puritan era, what was the punishment for being an actor in a traveling theater company?

   A) Execution
   B) To be whipped and put in stocks
   C) Hands cut off
   D) Imprisonment

'Blessed be the man that spares these stones, and cursed be he that moves my bones.' This curse appears above the grave of which man?

   A) William Shakespeare
   B) Henry VIII
   C) Leonardo da Vinci
   D) Sir Francis Drake

What did women rub on their faces to achieve silky skin?

   A) Cat's urine
   B) Nettles
   C) The blood of a freshly-killed cockerel
   D) Toads

147

Lady Jane Grey was Queen of England for how long?

A) 6 hours
B) 2 days
C) 9 days
D) 46 years

148

In the 17th century people were usually buried with a coin and a candle and what else?

A) A layer of bran to keep them comfortable
B) A cake in case they were hungry
C) A hammer to break open the coffin
D) A hunting-knife for self-defense

149

It was customary for executioners to hold up the head of the person they'd just beheaded to show to the crowd. On one occasion, the executioner tried to do this, only to be left holding a wig! Who was the person left without either a wig or a head?

A) Mary Queen Of Scots
B) Edward VI
C) Lady Jane Grey
D) Elizabeth I

Who did Guy Fawkes and co try to kill with their Gunpowder Plot?

A) Pope Gregory III
B) Queen Elizabeth I
C) King James I
D) King Charles I

150

How many barrels of gunpowder were discovered under the Houses of Parliament in 1605?

A) 36
B) 9
C) 120
D) 4,300

151

What was a 'snow dropper' in the 17th century?

A) Someone who stole your washing
B) An early type of washing machine
C) A pig thief
D) A dogwalker

152

153

Throughout the 1600s in Europe, nobles often held court whilst –?

A) In the bath
B) Naked
C) Picking their noses
D) Sitting on the toilet

154

The 1600s were a time where radical political groups flourished. One of them liked to cavort naked in public. They were known as the what?

A) Nudies
B) Bonkers
C) Ranters
D) Growlers

155

When the cook of Henry VIII's pal the Bishop of Rochester poisoned some of his guests, Henry ordered that the cook be –?

A) Released without charge
B) Forced to eat a ton of semolina pudding
C) Boiled alive in his own pot
D) Hanged and then turned into dog food

Between 1648 and 1653, the British Parliament was known as the what?

A) Backside Parliament
B) Booty Parliament
C) Buttock Parliament
D) Rump Parliament

What sort of person was a 'Fegge boy?'

A) A chimney sweep
B) A pickpocket
C) A highwayman
D) An executioner

Little boys were required to wear what until age six?

A) Petticoats
B) Bonnets
C) Bloomers
D) Earrings

159

Charles I's favorite joke was to pretend to eat what?

A) Dog excrement
B) Cabbage
C) His own arm
D) The court dwarf

160

What was particularly gruesome about the beheading of Mary Queen Of Scots?

A) It took three blows of the axe to sever her head
B) Her severed head was stolen by a stray dog and eaten
C) Her head spoke for nine hours after being cut off
D) She was beheaded with a kitchen knife instead of an axe

161

What day was traditionally used for executions?

A) Friday
B) Thursday
C) Monday
D) Sunday

The Tudors believed you could cure asthma by swallowing what?

162

A) Poisonous mushrooms
B) Raw eggs
C) A frog
D) The eyeballs of a dead dog

In 15th century France, a pig was executed for what reason?

163

A) Being an English spy
B) Eating a small child
C) Having a Catholic name
D) Farting in the King's face

It was illegal to be homeless in Tudor times. If you were caught, you would be whipped through the streets for your first offense. What would happen to you if you were caught a second time?

164

A) You'd have an ear cut off
B) You'd have your legs broken
C) You'd have your eyes gouged out
D) You'd be hanged

The Tudor and the Stuart Ages

165 At this time people thought toothache was caused by –?

A) Tooth fairies
B) Worms in the teeth
C) Bad breath
D) Lack of exercise

166 Christmas Pudding in the Stuart era had lots of ingredients including candied peel, raisins, sugar and spices. What other delicacies could be found in it?

A) Sulfur and marzipan
B) Chopped cow's tongue and chicken
C) Coconut and cream
D) Frogs and snails

167 What was the cure for jaundice?

A) Eat dog hair
B) Put drops of belladonna in your eyes
C) Walk on morning dew in bare feet
D) Cut two tench fish in half and wear them on your feet

The main component of gunpowder used in those days was saltpetre which was made up of what ingredients?

    A) Salt and Pepper
    B) Catgut
    C) Salted peanuts
    D) Bird droppings and human urine

168

A common device for cooking in those days was a type of wheel that turned meat. What drove the mechanism?

    A) A dog running inside the wheel
    B) A pig walking round
    C) A loom
    D) A hamster

169

What was a sin-eater?

    A) A person who ate dogs
    B) A devil-worshipper
    C) A person who ate a loaf of bread over a corpse to absorb the dead person's sins and enable them to enter heaven
    D) A terrible singer

170

171

In Jamaica in 1740, two doctors fought a duel in which both of them were killed. What was the cause of their dispute?

A) Whether the name 'Percival' was silly or not

B) Whether yellow fever was different than blackwater fever

C) Whether the human heart was in the center of the body or to the left

D) Whether malaria was carried by rats or mosquitoes

172

If you think your dad is bad, think of Alexis, who had the Russian leader Peter The Great for a dad. He used to get beaten up and dragged by the hair as a child, and later when he grew up, his dad called him 'worthless' and threatened not to let him become ruler. Then, to cap it all, in 1718, Peter had Alexis —?

A) Sent to live in a cave in freezing cold Siberia

B) Tortured and killed

C) Certified mad and sent to an asylum

D) Legally registered as a girl and forced to wear dresses

The Eighteenth Century

Why did gentlemen not wear trousers in 18th century Britain?

173

A) They were deemed too restrictive

B) They were only worn by women

C) It was a sign of being poor

D) They impeded the wearing of weapons

The Russian Czar, Peter III, became unpopular with his subjects because he liked to –?

174

A) Ride through the streets naked

B) Force peasants to fight bears at his parties

C) Fire big guns at all times of the day and night just because he liked how it sounded

D) Give incredibly long and boring speeches that everyone had to listen to

---

Peter III didn't impress his wife very much either. At the funeral of her mother, (the Empress Elizabeth), Peter behaved terribly. Which of these did he NOT do?

175

A) Burst out laughing

B) Stick his tongue out

C) Keep interrupting the priest

D) Urinate behind the altar

176 When Peter III wasn't disgracing himself at funerals, he was disgracing himself at banquets. One of his favorite jokes was to –?

    A) Throw food at his wife
    B) Pour wine over the heads of his waiters
    C) Puke on his most honored guest
    D) Belch the Russian National Anthem

---

177 And instead of giving his wife an heir to the throne, when Peter was with her in bed he would –?

    A) Light his farts
    B) Write letters to Santa Claus
    C) Flick snot at her
    D) Play with toy soldiers

---

178 Mary Toft shot to fame in England in 1726 when she apparently gave birth to –?

    A) A monkey
    B) The Messiah
    C) Rabbits
    D) A fully grown man

The Eighteenth Century

What did Princess Augusta do during her wedding ceremony in 1736?

A) Wet herself
B) Called her husband 'the ugliest scoundrel in the land'
C) Dropped dead
D) Threw up

The French philosopher, the Marquis de Sade, was famous for taking pleasure in cruelty. When he was finally sentenced to jail, he managed to escape by –?

A) Climbing through a toilet window
B) Digging a tunnel with a teaspoon
C) Bribing a guard
D) Hiding in a wagon loaded with manure

What did 'Night soil' men do throughout the 1700s?

A) Rob graves
B) Collect excrement from giant pools
C) Try to turn base metals into gold
D) Escort condemned men to their place of execution

182 **W**hat was a common cure for bad breath?

A) Wearing roasted pieces of turnip behind the ears

B) Wearing garlands of garlic

C) Licking toads

D) Drinking cat's urine

183 **T**he Scots poet Robbie Burns once wrote an ode to –?

A) Excrement

B) A worm

C) Tuberculosis

D) A louse

184 **B**enjamin Franklin is famous for saying, at the signing of the American Declaration of Independence, 'We must indeed all hang together, or, most assuredly, we shall all hang separately.' But he also wrote an essay called –?

A) Never Wash Behind Your Ears Gladly

B) Speak With Your Mouth Full, And Loudly

C) Fart Proudly

D) Pick Your Nose Openly

The Eighteenth Century

When George Washington became General of the Continental Army in the US, he declined any salary and asked instead merely for an expense account to cover his food and so on. How much did he manage to spend in the eight years he was in the job (in today's money)?

- **A)** $312
- **B)** $120,000
- **C)** $100,000,000
- **D)** $4,000,000

George Washington had false teeth made partly from –?

- **A)** Gold
- **B)** Hippopotamus ivory
- **C)** Crocodile bones
- **D)** Paper

What was called 'The Disease Of Kings' at this time?

- **A)** Alcoholism
- **B)** Insanity
- **C)** Gout
- **D)** Baldness

188 **W**hy did 18th century sailors tap their biscuits on the table before eating them?

A) To ward off evil spirits
B) To show their respect for the King
C) To check if they were soft because soft biscuits were a sign of a deadly fungus
D) To knock insects out of them

189 **I**n the 18th century, what was a valid reason for a man to divorce his wife?

A) Her feet were too small
B) She couldn't cook
C) If he found that she was ugly under her makeup
D) She had body odor

190 **D**uring the Peterloo massacre of 1819, a yeoman with a sabre went to chop a man's head. How was the man saved?

A) He was wearing a wig that flew off
B) A bible he was carrying under his cap
C) His hat was tin-lined
D) By a lump of cheese under his hat

What was King George IV's nickname for his wife Queen Caroline?

A) Sweet Pea
B) The Dragon
C) The Fiend
D) The Witch

Until the mid 1800s people thought all diseases were caused by 'The Four Humors.' They were blood, phlegm, black bile and what?

A) Green bile
B) Yellow bile
C) Red bile
C) Melancholy

What claim to fame does Spencer Perceval have? He was the:

A) Last man to be publicly hanged in Britain
B) First man to be killed by a motor car in Britain
C) First convicted British serial killer
D) Only British Prime Minister ever to be assassinated

194 **T**wo famous grave robbers operated in Britain in the 19th century, Mr Burke and Mr Hare. What did they do with the bodies of their victims?

A) Ate them

B) Stuffed them and displayed them in glass cases

C) Sold them to surgeons

D) Chopped them into pieces and threw them into The Thames

---

195 **W**hat was the name of the notorious Highwayman Dick Turpin's horse?

A) Snowball

B) Silver

C) Black Bess

D) Red Rum

---

196 **W**hat did people pay one penny to watch at St Mary Of Bethlehem in London every Sunday until 1815?

A) Strip shows

B) Lunatics

C) Cock-fighting

D) Bare knuckle boxing

The smell of sewage outside The House Of Commons in London in 1858 forced Members of Parliament to order the construction of a vast network of sewers. What was the smell known as?

A) The Terrible Stench
B) Queen Victoria's Pants
C) The Mighty Whiff
D) The Great Stink

What percentage of people admitted into asylums as this time were not mad at all, just poor?

A) 75%
B) 95%
C) 25%
D) 4%

King George IV and King William IV both died of what?

A) Eating food that had gone bad
B) Bungled operations
C) Over-drinking
D) Diarrhea

200

False teeth at this time often came from which source?

- **A)** Young children
- **B)** Dead soldiers
- **C)** Pigs
- **D)** Dogs

201

How did the MP William Huskisson get into the record books whilst attending the opening of the Liverpool to Manchester railway in 1830? He was the:

- **A)** First man to get train sick
- **B)** First man to complain about the food on a train
- **C)** First man to rob a train
- **D)** First man to die on the railroads

202

Why did Napoleon always have his hand under his jacket?

- **A)** He was protecting his heart
- **B)** He wanted to keep his hand warm
- **C)** He was paranoid about losing his wallet
- **D)** He suffered from a nervous itch

In many places in Europe husbands were allowed to beat their wives with a stick as long as:

A) The stick was no wider than the husband's thumb
B) It was not a Sunday
C) They said sorry afterwards
D) It was before ten o'clock in the evening

In what year were the first public toilets built in London?

A) 1801
B) 1852
C) 1823
D) 1897

In 1845, at the funeral of President Jackson, officials upset by constant swearing had to forcibly remove the President's –?

A) Wife
B) Elderly mother
C) Parrot
D) Bookmaker

206

A favorite pastime in the 1800s was trying to kill Queen Victoria. In total, how many assassination attempts did she survive?

- **A)** 3
- **B)** 8
- **C)** 15
- **D)** 129

207

The shortest war in history took place in 1896 between which two sides?

- **A)** Britain and France
- **B)** Britain and Zanzibar
- **C)** Britain and Iceland
- **D)** United States and Mexico

208

How long did this war last?

- **A)** 38 minutes
- **B)** 1 hour 2 minutes
- **C)** 3 hours 32 minutes
- **D)** 2 days

The fearsome French Emperor Napoleon was afraid of —?

   A) The dark
   B) Spiders
   C) Cats
   D) Being buried alive

In 1842 the president of Mexico, Antonio de Santa Anna, held a state funeral for his —?

   A) Dog
   B) Wife's dog
   C) Childhood innocence
   D) Severed leg

The German doctor Max von Pettenkofer was sure that cholera was caused by chemicals. He was so sure it wasn't passed from person to person that he —?

   A) Locked himself in a room with 10 cholera patients for a year
   B) Drank the urine of a cholera patient
   C) Drank the diarrhea of a cholera patient
   D) Drank from a well suspected to be infected with cholera

212

A large amount of the Oxford English Dictionary was written by –?

    A) A certified lunatic
    B) Prisoners of war
    C) A serial killer
    D) Queen Victoria

213

I n 1890 in New York, William Kemmler became the first person to –?

    A) Fly
    B) Be successfully treated with antibiotics
    C) Die in a car crash
    D) Die in the electric chair

214

W hich of these weapons was NOT first used during the American Civil War?

    A) Landmine
    B) Tank
    C) Observation balloon
    D) Machine gun

The First World War

World War I was triggered when Archduke Franz Ferdinand was murdered. Which of these events led to him being shot?

A) His driver took a wrong turn and went straight down the road that an assassin happened to be walking along

B) His butler invited a man with a gun into the house for a glass of water

C) Franz bet a ranting man that he didn't have the guts to shoot him

D) Franz ordered his bodyguards to release a man and give him his gun back after they had overpowered him

---

An American was caught spying for Germany during World War I after his socks were tested and found to contain what?

A) Invisible ink

B) Pollen from Germany

C) A book of codes written in microscopically small writing

D) Dynamite

217 A lot of the explosives used in WWI were made from what?

A) Horse manure
B) The fillings of dead soldiers
C) Peanuts
D) The fat of dead animals

218 How many men from their own side did the British shoot for deserting in WWI?

A) 218
B) 6
C) 44
D) 0

219 What, in WWI, was a 'toffee apple'?

A) An apple covered in toffee
B) A part of a trench given aside to going to the toilet
C) A grenade
D) A mortar

The Tank, used for the first time in WWI, was originally called –?

A) The Willie
B) The Billy-Boy
C) The Bad Boy
D) The Iron Horse

On a tour of duty at the Western Front, where the worst of the fighting was, what percentage of men sent out were either killed or wounded?

A) 3%
B) 55%
C) 21%
D) 86%

By the end of the war, how many machine guns did Britain have on the Western Front alone?

A) 250
B) 52,358
C) 7,234
D) 832,455

The First World War

223

In total, the war lasted from August 1914 till November 1918. If you averaged out the total number of shells fired, you find that throughout those four years and four months, a shell was fired every —?

- **A)** Fifty minutes
- **B)** Minute
- **C)** Ten minutes
- **D)** Two seconds

224

The British Army Medical Corps supplied how many glass eyes to people during the war?

- **A)** 120
- **B)** 3,657
- **C)** 22,386
- **D)** 122,498

225

Which of these was the nickname for a giant German gun?

- **A)** Big Brenda
- **B)** Big Glenda
- **C)** Big Bertha
- **D)** Big Susan

The First World War

The oldest British soldier to be injured in WWI was how old?

A) 84

B) 51

C) 68

D) 32

Which of these did MI5 entrust to carry secret messages?

A) Monks

B) Boy scouts

C) Nuns

D) Girl guides

Which of these was NOT against the law after the passing of the Defense Of The Realm Act during World War I?

A) Speaking on the telephone in a foreign language

B) Hanging about under railway bridges

C) Buying binoculars without asking for permission

D) Whispering to a man aged under fifty

The First World War

229 **M**any soldiers on the front line were killed during the heavy fighting at The Somme. One, who miraculously survived when his dugout took a direct hit from a shell, later played an important part in World War II. Who was he?

    A) Winston Churchill
    B) Adolf Hitler
    C) Franklin D Roosevelt
    D) Lenin

230 **W**hat happened to the dogs that the Soviets trained to blow up tanks with mines strapped to their backs?

    A) The dogs only recognized Soviet tanks and blew them up instead of enemy tanks
    B) The mines were so heavy that the dogs would refuse to move
    C) The mines did not go off under the tanks and the dogs would return to their handlers when the mines were due to explode
    D) The dogs were sold to the Germans for breeding

Kaiser Wilhelm of Germany could have been killed before the war even started. What close shave did he survive?

231

- **A)** He was hit by lightning
- **B)** He was the sole survivor of a fire that killed 36 other people
- **C)** He had the tip of his cigarette shot off by Annie Oakley
- **D)** He was shot in the heart by a British agent but survived because the bullet hit the silver cigarette case he carried in his breast pocket

---

How many people were killed in The Battle Of The Somme?

232

- **A)** 1,300,000
- **B)** 30,000
- **C)** 128,000
- **D)** 1,000

Who was called 'The Butcher Of Gallipoli?'

233

- **A)** Winston Churchill
- **B)** Archduke Franz Ferdinand
- **C)** Kaiser Wilhelm
- **D)** Lenin

234 Which of the following was exempt from serving in the war?

   A) Lawyers
   B) Teachers
   C) Electricians
   D) People over six feet tall

235 The British Government created a cartoon character aimed at showing the dangers of giving away secrets. What was the character called?

   A) Mr Gob
   B) Mr Blabber Box
   C) Miss Leaky Mouth
   D) Miss Chatter-knickers

236 Heinrich Himmler, the head of the much feared Nazi SS, was once a –?

   A) Circus master
   B) Chicken farmer
   C) Geography teacher
   D) Ice cream van driver

Which of these is NOT true?

A) Adolf Hitler didn't drink alcohol

B) Adolf Hitler didn't smoke

C) Adolf Hitler didn't have a silly moustache

D) Adolf Hitler ate meat

What was the name of the American plane that dropped an atomic bomb on the Japanese city of Hiroshima?

A) The Dark Destroyer

B) The Enola Gay

C) The Fat Boy

D) Bock's Car

Three days after attacking Hiroshima, the Americans dropped another atomic bomb on the Japanese city of Nagasaki. But Nagasaki was only selected at the last minute because the original target city was shrouded in smog. Which city had the Americans originally intended to bomb?

A) Tokyo

B) Kokura

C) Kyoto

D) Yokohama

240 The Russian Leader Josif Djugashvili changed his name to Stalin – what does 'Stalin' mean?

A) Man Of Steel
B) Man Of Gold
C) Man Of Iron
D) Man Of The People

241 Which British celebrity did an Italian newspaper claim had been killed in The Blitz?

A) Winston Churchill
B) The Queen Mother
C) The Loch Ness Monster
D) George V

242 How was British Prime Minister Winston Churchill nearly killed in 1942?

A) He was injured by a German bomb during the Blitz
B) The Germans tried to plant an explosive device in his cigar
C) His plane was almost shot down by the Royal Air Force
D) He was bitten by a scorpion whilst visiting troops in North Africa

Polish troops fighting at Monte Cassino brought what into battle with them?

A) A brown bear
B) A goat
C) Poisonous snakes
D) An elephant

243

At the start of the war, how much were British soldiers paid per day?

A) 10p
B) 2p
C) 90p
D) 18p

244

The British Government knew that there would be a lot of casualties in the forthcoming war, so shortly after war was declared they began stockpiling what?

A) False legs
B) Wood for coffins
C) Cardboard coffins
D) Lime to pour over dead bodies to make them dissolve

245

246 The Italian Fascist leader Mussolini, at the outbreak of World War II, described the Italian flag as –?

    A) A rag to be planted on a dunghill
    B) A lesson to be driven through Britain's heart
    C) A banner of blood and tears
    D) Nicer than any other flag in Europe

247 What did Mussolini call 1922, the year he came to power?

    A) Year One
    B) The Year Of Mussolini
    C) The Year The World Changed
    D) The Year The War Began

248 What sticky end did Mussolini meet?

    A) Thrown from the top of a building into the street
    B) Beheaded and dragged through the streets
    C) Tied to a tank and dragged through the streets
    D) Shot and hanged upside down in the street

The Second World War

A German submarine was sunk by an exploding what?

- **A)** Dolphin
- **B)** Crab
- **C)** Toilet
- **D)** Letter

A lot of children were evacuated from big cities into the countryside during the war. How many were left unclaimed when the war finished?

- **A)** 9
- **B)** 4,600
- **C)** 38,000
- **D)** 442,000

What were 'Gulags?'

- **A)** Carrier pigeons
- **B)** Lightning fast attacks carried out by German 'storm troopers'
- **C)** Nazi concentration camps
- **D)** Russian forced labor camps

Why were the tops of pillar boxes in Britain painted green or yellow during World War II?

A) A green top meant post for within the country, a yellow top meant post for overseas

B) Because if mustard gas was dropped the paint would be stained and alert the authorities

C) To hide them from German bombers

D) A green top meant post was being collected, a yellow one meant it wasn't

Leon Trotsky was a politician who disapproved of the Russian leader Stalin and made the mistake of criticizing him. Not long afterwards, Trotsky was found dead with –?

A) An ice-pick in his head

B) A red hot poker up his backside

C) His notebooks stuffed down his throat

D) The words 'Stalin Rules' carved on his forehead

Which of these was NOT a nickname for a gas mask?

A) Dicky-birds
B) Nosebag
C) Canaries
D) Humbles

254

Hitler was once sentenced to prison in 1923 for what?

A) Treason
B) Shoplifting
C) Armed robbery
D) Tax evasion

255

In order to save energy, The Ministry of Fuel suggested that the water in British baths should be how deep?

A) 12.7 cm/5 in
B) 6.4 cm/2.5 in
C) 18 cm/7 in
D) 26.5 cm/10.5 in

256

257 The Americans knew the war could be won with a nuclear weapon. The first nuclear reaction which led to the creation of the bomb took place where?

A) On a remote island in the Pacific
B) In a Washington laboratory
C) On a squash court in Chicago
D) On a glacier in Alaska

258 With what did the RAF destroy German dams?

A) Trained dolphins
B) Bouncing bombs
C) Infiltrators
D) Swimming tanks

259 The Germans created a flying bomb called the V1 – V for Vergeltungswaffen. What does this mean?

A) Vengeance weapon
B) Flying bomb
C) We are the champions
D) Sitting ducks

What were the last words in Anne Frank's diary, written three months before her death in Belsen concentration camp?

 A) I hope the Nazis lose

 B) All people are good

 C) I'm really hungry

 D) Help me

Boots were in short supply during World War II. How did the Germans get the boots of dead, frozen Russian soldiers?

 A) They built a bonfire and thawed them out

 B) They sawed off their legs

 C) They cut off the boots and sewed them back up

 D) They carried the rotting corpses with them until the boots came off easily

What color was Allied troops' toilet tissue?

 A) Red so you could use it to mop up blood

 B) Blue to match the sky

 C) White for peace

 D) Khaki brown to camouflage it

Other Titles

There are many other exciting quiz
and puzzle books in the IntelliQuest range,
and your QUIZMO electronic unit
knows the answers to them all!

You can order from your
local bookshop or on-line bookseller.

For a full listing of current titles
(and ISBN numbers) see:

www.intelliquestbooks.com

**LAGOON
BOOKS**